Moon Magick

COLOURING BOOK

TAP INTO YOUR MYSTICAL POTENTIAL

chartwell
books

Connect to the Moon's mystical power!

The magnificent, magical Moon is often referred to as the Triple Goddess, characterized as a female passing through life's phases—from young woman to adult woman and mother, and, finally, to the old woman. From ancient times to the present, humans have looked to the night sky for guidance and to tap into the Moon's magic. In every phase of the Moon's journey, it can provide insight, renewal, and meditative calm.

The act of colouring can also be meditative in and of itself, bringing about calmness just through the simple act of focusing your creativity and thoughts on a single colouring exercise. The rhythm and tactile experience help us connect to our body as it disconnects us from the computers, phones, and screens that fill our daily life.

Like the Moon, colouring is accessible for everyone. Even if you lack artistic instruction or experience, you can create beautiful, finished pieces. Having guidelines eases performance anxiety for many, and being able to add our own colours helps make the experience more personal. Despite what you may have learned about art and colour in your lifetime, there is no right or wrong way to colour, and there is no right or wrong way to use this book; you have the freedom to colour it in however you wish and in whatever way works best for you.

The act of meditative colouring combined with the beautiful lunar subject matter in this book are meant to work together to create a powerful, creative experience. Enjoy!

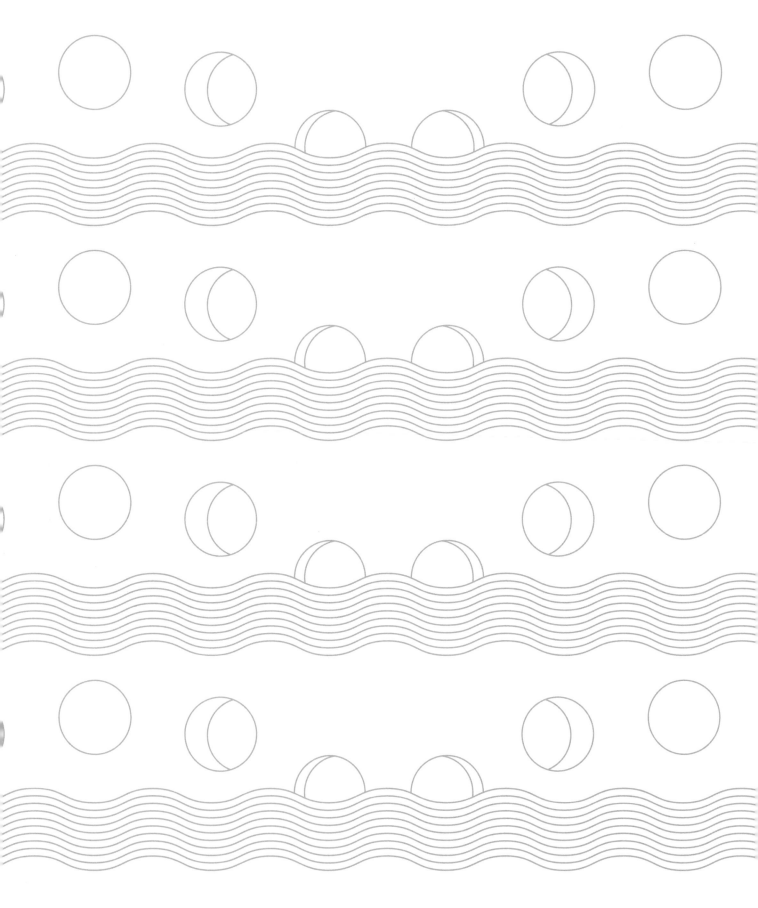

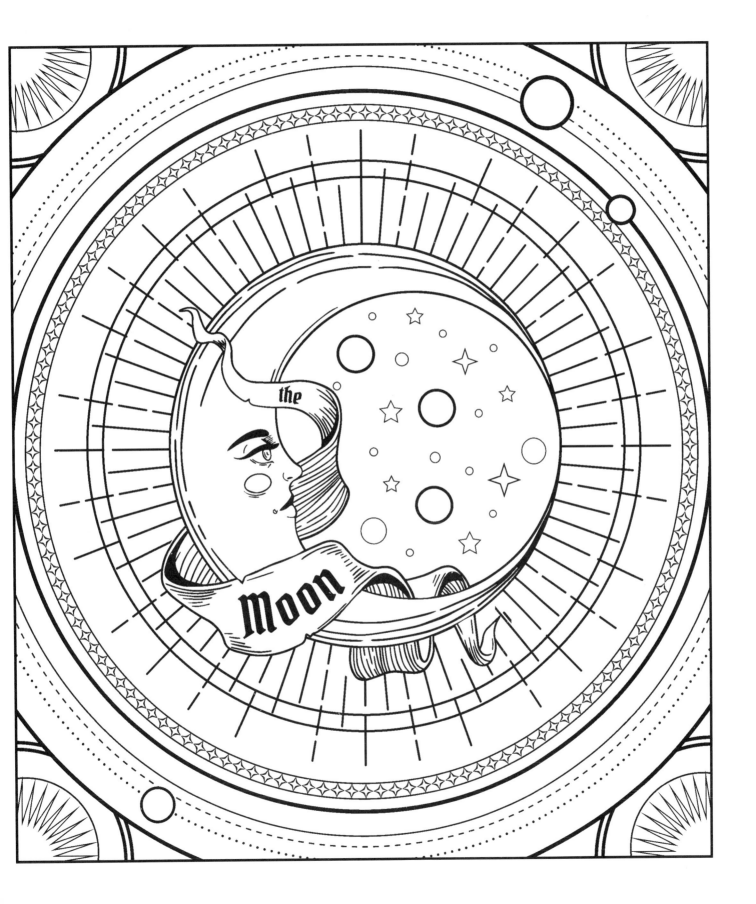

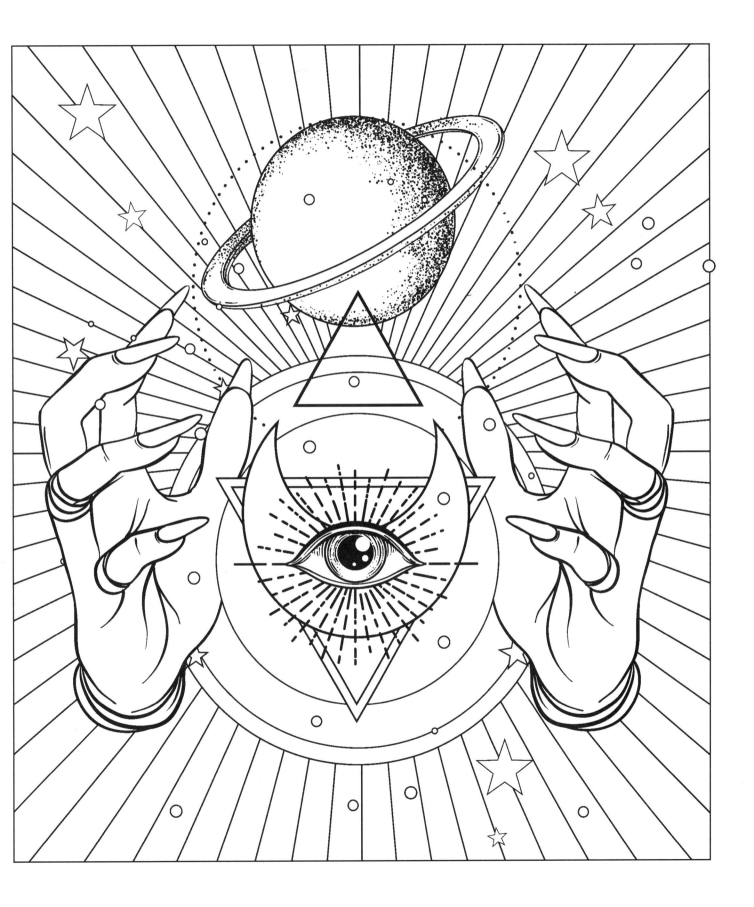

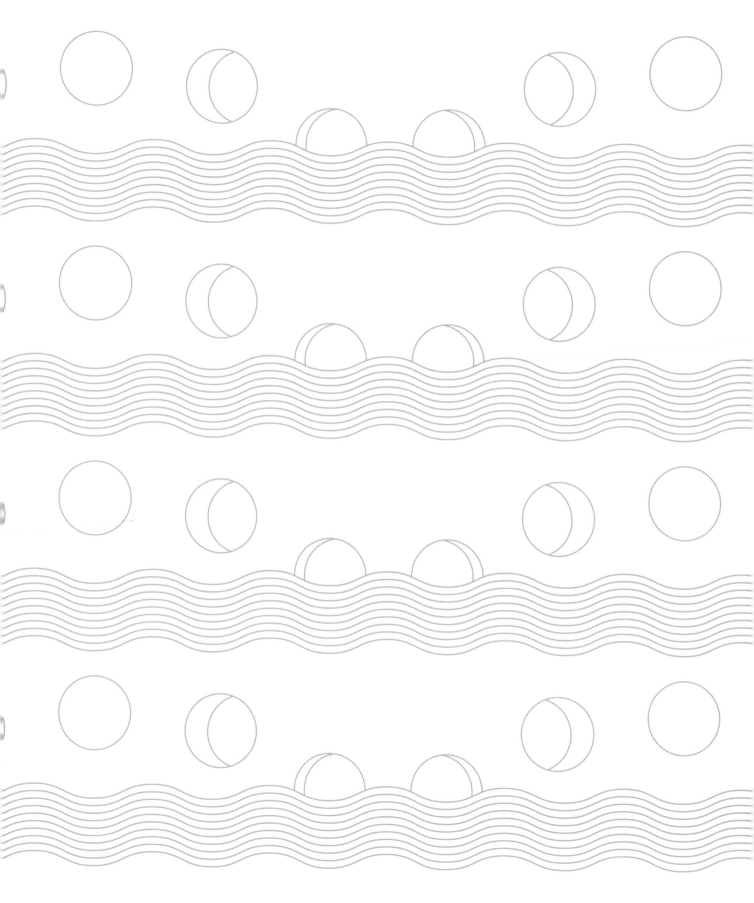

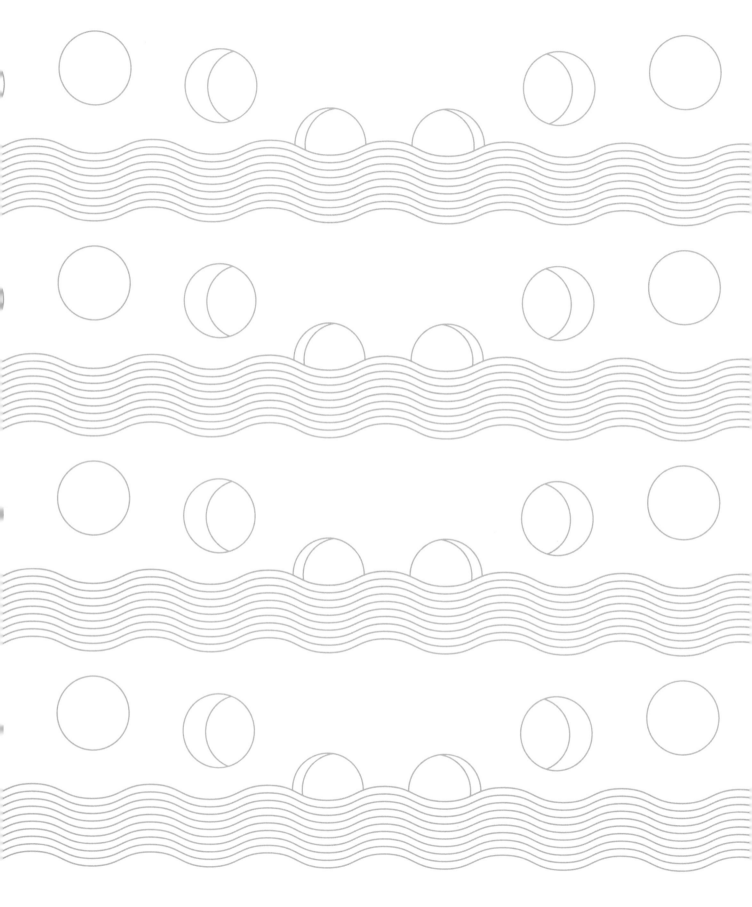

Quarto

Published in 2021 by Chartwell Books, an imprint of The Quarto Group
142 West 36th Street, 4th Floor New York, NY 10018 USA
www.Quarto.com

10 9 8 7 6 5 4

Chartwell titles are also available at discount for retail, wholesale, promotional,
and bulk purchase. For details, contact the Special Sales Manager by email at
specialsales@quarto.com or by mail at The Quarto Group, Attn: Special Sales
Manager, 100 Cummings Center Suite 265D, Beverly, MA 01915, USA.

ISBN: 978-0-7858-4158-6

Printed in China

Publisher: Wendy Friedman
Editorial Director: Betina Cochran
Creative Director: Pauline Molinari
Designer: Sue Boylan
Editor: Meredith Mennitt
All stock design elements ©Shutterstock